Rocky, lava coastline near Makapu‘u, O‘ahu

Hawaiian pond near the shore at Hanalei, Kaua'i

PLANTS INDEX: page location, Hawaiian or English name, and native or alien species.
(I) = Indigenous native plant, arrived in Hawai'i without human help, also native elsewhere;
(E) = Endemic native plant, unique organism evolved from an indigenous Hawaiian species;
(P) = Polynesian introduction, brought to Hawai'i by people during the pre-contact period;
(R) = Recent alien, post-contact introduction, brought to Hawai'i by people after 1778.

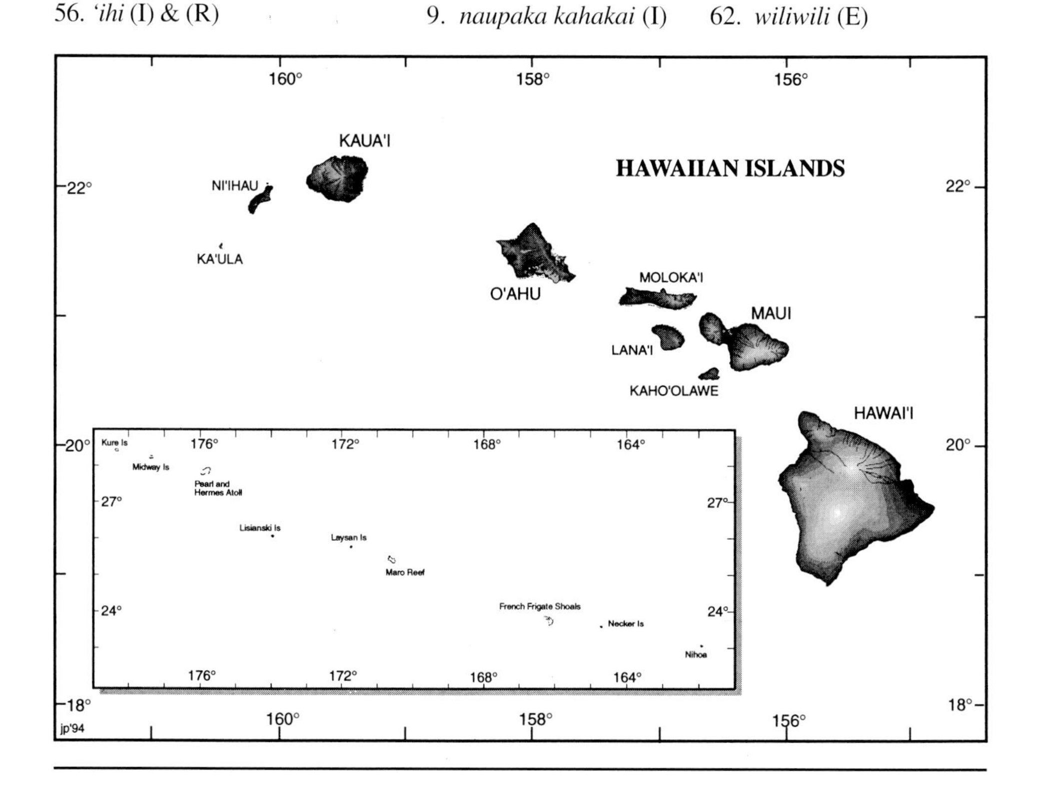

Pōhuehue
Beach Morning Glory (I)
Ipomoea pes-caprae subsp. *brasiliensis*
Family: Convolvulaceae

Description

Pōhuehue, also known as the beach morning glory, is a perennial seashore vine. It has thick, smooth, 2 to 3 inch long leaves and pinkish-red, bell-shaped flowers. The small fruit capsules usually contain four, saltwater-tolerant, dark-colored seeds; and the stems lay prostrate, extending out over the ground as much as 30 to 100 feet.

Distribution

Formerly more common, this creeper is still found in sizable clumps along many sandy beaches of Hawai'i. It is believed that *pōhuehue* arrived in Hawai'i without human help, and is therefore referred to as a native plant. However, because it is also native along many other tropical beaches of the world, it is classified as an indigenous plant in Hawai'i and not endemic (which means restricted to a particular area such as Hawai'i). Below, *pōhuehue* covers the foreground of a beach on the south shore of Moloka'i. In the distance lies Lāna'i, with tradewind clouds covering the summit region of that island.

Uses

In times of famine in ancient Hawai'i, the long roots of *pōhuehue* were cooked and eaten, however this wild food can be poisonous! Ancient Hawaiian surfers sometimes slapped the stems on the sea surface and offered special chants believing that the surf would thus rise.

Hinahina, hinahina kū kahakai
Heliotropium anomalum **(I)**
Heliotropium anomalum var. *argenteum* **(E)**
Family: Boraginaceae

Description

Hinahina means very gray colored, an apparent reference to the slender, 1 to 2 inch long leaves of this low-lying, native, perennial beach plant. Tiny white hairs cover the leaves giving the plant its characteristic silverish appearance (var.. *argenteum*). The small aromatic flowers of *hinahina* are white with a yellowish center.. They are arranged in one-sided coiled spikes on forked stalks.

Distribution

The seeds *hinahina* are able to tolerate long periods of immersion in salt water. Its natural habitat is the dry, sandy beach environment. It is often found growing near the tidal zone (see page 6 where it covers much of the ground near the shore at Kalaupapa, Moloka'i). The variety *argenteum* of this species is endemic to the Hawaiian Islands.

Uses

The beach heliotrope, *hinahina*, is the island flower of arid, wind-swept Kaho'olawe. The grayish to silvery leaves and attractive flowers of *hinahina* are sometimes used in *lei* making. When the leaves of *koko'olau* plants (*Bidens* spp.) are not available, the succulent leaves of *hinahina* are sometimes brewed in the process of producing a tonic tea.

***Naupaka kahakai* (I)**
Beach *Naupaka*
Scaevola taccada
Family: Goodeniaceae

Description

Naupaka kahakai is an indigenous shrub that may grow upward, densely branched, to heights of 8 to12 feet. The succulent leaves are 3 to 5 inches long and wider at the tip than at the base. The whitish flowers are about ¾ of an inch long and appear as though they might have been torn in half, with five petals remaining (the flower with six petals shown here is unusual). The fleshly, white berries are about ½ an inch wide.

Distribution

Naupaka kahakai is a native coastal shrub throughout the tropical and subtropical Pacific and Indian Ocean regions, including Hawai'i. The fruits are tolerant of saltwater, buoyant, and easily dispersed. Currents and tides move the fruits across the Pacific and Indian Oceans. Interestingly, the fruits can float in the sea for many months, some retaining their ability to germinate when washed ashore after more than a year in the sea.

Uses

Occasionally in the past in Hawai'i, the whitish fruits of *naupaka kahakai* were eaten, and the rough bark has been useful as medicinal material. According to one old story, the flower was torn into its present "half" shape by a Hawaiian maiden who believed her lover had been unfaithful. She demanded that he prove his fidelity by finding another "whole flower" of this plant. Sadly, he was unsuccessful and was said to have died of a broken heart. *Naupaka kahakai* is shown on page 8, and below, with the grayish *hinahina* (*Heliotropium anomalum*).

Orange fruits of Pū-Hala

***Hala*, *pū hala* (I)**
Screwpine
Pandanus tectorius
Family: Pandanaceae

Description

Hala is a widely branching species with individual male and female trees. It may grow as tall as 30 feet supported by aerial prop roots. Its leaves are long, thin, fibrous, thorny, and pointed. *Hala* produces colorful fruit clusters that are sometimes mistaken for pineapples. The yellowish male flowers are produced on fragrant spikes.

Distribution

Hala is indigenous in Hawai'i. Thus, it is native but not unique to these islands. In fact, the species *Pandanus tectorius* is widespread, found along or near the coast of most tropical Pacific islands. Fossils of its fruit more than a million years have been found along the north coast of Kaua'i. Although it is usually associated with coastal environments, *hala* can also be found growing farther inland up to elevations of almost 2,000 feet.

Uses

Hala has many traditional uses in Hawai'i. The starchy fruit and bracts of the fragrant male flowers were occasionally eaten. The long, dried leaves, known as *lauhala* are or were used as pliable weaving material to make floormats, hats, baskets, fans, sandals, pillows, thatch, and durable sails for canoes. Fresh fruits were used in *lei*, and old dry ones were used as brushes to apply various dyes to *kapa,* the tradtional cloth of the Polynesian culture.

ʻŌhelo kai, ʻaeʻae **(I)**
Lycium sandwicense
Family: Solanaceae

Description

ʻŌhelo kai ("sea berry") or *ʻaeʻae* ("at the tide") are the two most common names for this very low-lying beach shrub. It has pale bark and stiff branches, which can root when lying on the ground. The narrow leaves of this plant are about an inch long, succulent, and light green. The solitary flowers are about ¼ of an inch long, light colored, almost lavender, with four petals joined together in the tube. They are borne at the leaf axils. The juicy red fruit has a salty, but edible, pulp. Like other members of Solanaceae (variously known as the tomato, potato, or nightshade family), the fruit of *ʻōhelo kai* contains numerous flattish seeds.

Distribution

Although relatively rare today, *ʻōhelo kai* is still found along the rocky shorelines of the more arid coastal regions of Hawaiʻi. Normally it grows within reach of the sea spray. This native halophytic (salt-tolerant) plant is indigenous. Therefore it native to Hawaiʻi, but is also native to other tropical areas including Rapa, Tonga, and the Juan Fernandez Islands.

Uses

During the drier periods, livestock may graze on the leaves of this beach plant. The salty berry of *ʻōhelo-kai* or *ʻaeʻae* is edible, but it is not very tasty. In some uplands of Hawaiʻi, other plants (*Vaccinium* spp.) with edible red fruit, are known in Hawaiian as *ʻōhelo.*

***'Ilima, 'ilima kū kahakai, 'ilima papa* (I)**
Sida fallax
Family: Malvaceae

Description

'Ilima is a small, low-lying plant with trailing branches. The leaves are light green, oblong or heart-shaped, and blunt or pointed; they have serrated margins and are about 1 inch long. The attractive flowers are yellow-orange, five-petaled, and about ½ to 1 inch in diameter.

Distribution

'Ilima is a common beach plant in Hawai'i. It can be found growing along many of the drier coastal areas in small prostrate clumps covering open sandy or rocky places near the sea or perched on cliffs above the ocean. *Sida fallax* is indigenous in Hawai'i. In fact, this plant is found in the drier regions of many other tropical Pacific islands. For example, low-lying Wake Island in Micronesia is known in Marshallese as *Enen Kio* (*'ilima* island) because this dry coastal plant is so common there.

Uses

The lovely flowers of *'ilima* have long been used in Hawai'i for *lei* making. Today an imitation orange paper *lei* is often used in place of a freshly woven *lei* of true *'ilima* flowers. As a source of medicine, the flowers of *'ilima* were sometimes used to treat general debility. Occasionally the juice of pressed flowers was given to children, and pregnant women sometimes ate the flowers until the time of childbirth.

***Koko*, *'akoko* (E)** Chamaesyce degeneri
Beach spurge Family: Euphorbiaceae

Description

Koko or *'akoko,* the beach spurge, is a small, sprawling, mat-like, native plant. It has succulent, rounded, inch-long, opposing leaves that often become reddish when damaged or prior to dropping off the plant. The flowers are very small, pale yellow, and form at the leaf axils and branch tips. Unlike other native Hawaiian plants that belong to the spurge family, this coastal plant is not woody.

Distribution

Koko is one of fifteen endemic Hawaiian species in the genus *Chamaesyce*. All of these species were formerly classified as belonging to the large genus *Euphorbia*. The general Hawaiian name for these plants (*koko*) refers to the reddish, blood-colored appearance of some leaves. The beach spurge is found on Hawai'i, Mau'i, Moloka'i, O'ahu, Kaua'i, and Ni'ihau, where it grows on sand dunes, in clay soils, or on outcrops along the drier coastlines. Unfortunately *koko* is much less common today than in the past. The specific scientific name of the species (*degeneri*) honors Otto Degener who, contributed much to our knowledge of the Hawaiian flora.

Nohu, nohunohu **(I)**
Puncture vine
Tribulus cistoides
Family: Zygophyllaceae

Description

Nohu is a small, low-lying, perennial herb. The stems are usually less than 3 feet long and produce pairs of leaves 1 to 5 inches long. Each leaf has approximately 6 pairs of leaflets, each about ½ inch long. Both stems and leaves are covered with many tiny hairs. The flowers are yellow, have five petals, and are about an inch in diameter. The fruit is about 1/3 of an inch in diameter, has 3 to 5 lobes, and several sharp spines. In fact, *nohu* is one of the very few prickly native Hawaiian plants.

Distribution

Sometimes referred to as *mahukona* violet because of the flowering fragrance, the native *nohu* is considered to be an indigenous plant; in other words, it is also native to many other dry tropical coastal regions of the world, but reached the Hawaiian Islands without human assistance. It can be found on both the high and low islands of Hawai`i. Beachcombers beware: the spiny fruits of *nohu* can be quite painful when stepped on by the barefoot hiker. Indeed, the name, *nohu* also refers the spiny scorpionfish in Hawaii (*Scopaenopsis cacopsis*).

***Pā'ū-o-Hi'iaka, kākua-o-Hi'iaka, kaupo'o* (I)**
Jacquemontia ovalifolia
Family: Convolvulaceae

Description

This small, native member of the morning-glory family, Convolvulaceae, is a perennial herb. Somewhat woody at the base, this low-lying, sprawling plant spreads out as a trailing vine to cover bare rock and soil. The stems may reach up to 10 feet in length, often rooting at the nodes. The relatively thick and inverted leaves are about 1 inch long. Some plants in this species produce an abundance of tiny whitish hairs on their leaves. The flowers are about ½ inch wide and purple to whitish (see photographs on pages 16 and 17); they are in bloom mainly from December to July. The small tan to brown capsules hold 1 to 4 seeds.

Distribution

The species *Jacquemontia ovalifolia* is indigenous in Hawai'i, as well in areas in Mexico, the West Indies, and Africa. However, the unique subspecies, *Jacquemontia ovalifolia* subsp. *sandwicensis*, is endemic to Hawai'i. This subspecies is adapted to the drier lowland regions on the leeward sides of the Hawaiian Islands, more often today near the shore. Like many native Hawaiian species, in the past it was more common in several inland and coastal habitats; but residential and commercial impact has taken its toll on this interesting plant.

Uses

According to Hawaiian legend, this plant was given its name by Pele, the Fire Goddess of the volcanoes. Pele called it the "skirt of Hi`iaka" (*Pā`ū-o-Hi`iaka*) because she once returned from a lengthy morning of fishing and found her baby sister (Hi`iaka) on the beach, covered by the trailing stems of this plant. This overgrowth of the sprawling vine protected the child from the strong rays of the sun. The roots and leaves of this plant were reportedly served as food in ancient Hawai'i. Medicinally, the plant was used as a cathartic and for treating babies that had suffered from a common mouth ailment, thrush (*ea*).

Two native coastal plants, *pā'ū-o-Hi'iaka* (*Jacquemontia ovalifolia* subsp. *sandwicensis*) and *'ilima* (*Sida fallax*) intertwined on a sandy beach in Hawai'i.

***Pōhinahina, kolokolo kahakai* (I)** *Vitex rotundifolia*
Beach vitex Family: Verbenaceae

Description

Pōhinahina is a low-lying shrub that barely grows more than 2 feet above the ground. Its name most likely refers to the grayish or silvery appearance of its leaves; its other Hawaiian name, *kolokolo kahakai*, means beach creeper. The light green leaves of this coastal plant are 1 to 2 inches long with hairs on both sides. They are arranged on the stems in pairs opposite each other. The summer-blooming flowers are blue or purplish, about an inch long, and are usually found at the branch tips. The small globular fruits are dark red or black.

Distribution

This indigenous Hawaiian beach plant is also native to several widely separated regions, such as parts of southern Japan, some areas of India, and many tropical Pacific Islands. *Pōhinahina* was probably still quite common not so long ago in Hawai'i, especially in coastal dunes. However, extensive development of residential and commercial structures along the coasts in recent decades has reduced the geographical distribution of this and many other native seashore plants of Hawai'i. In some cases these plants have become endangered, or unfortunately they have become extinct and are thus gone forever! This sad situation is especially true for the unique, endemic species which are, or were, found only in the Hawaiian Islands.

***Nehe* (E)**
Lipochaeta integrifolia
Family: Asteraceae

Description

The native *nehe* is a low-lying, sprawling, perennial plant. Its succulent leaves are about one inch long and have white hairs. The branches of *nehe* may grow up above the ground more than a foot out of its mat-like ground cover. Its yellowish flower clusters, approximately ½ inch wide, are produced at the tips of the branches. Like so many other species in the very large sunflower or aster family, the flower clusters of *nehe*, which appear to be single flowers, are actually composed of many small flowers (florets) arranged in a central disk. The disk is surrounded by an outer ring of florets that have attractive marginal, petal-like rays.

Distribution

Nehe is still rather common and can usually be found growing very near the coast along with *naupaka kahakai*, *hinahina*, *'ilima*, *pā'ū-o-Hi'iaka*, *alena*, and other native Hawaiian coastal plants. Botanists have classified over twenty species in the genus *Lipochaeta*; all of them are endemic to Hawai'i, and all are known in Hawaiian as *nehe*. The different species of *nehe* in Hawai'i are distributed into a variety of environments, including the high mountains, lava flows, and along the seashore. One closely related species is native to the Galapagos Islands; and another is found in the Loyalty Islands and Vanuatu of Melanesia. *Lipochaeta* is closely related to *Wollastonia* (formerly called *Wedelia*), a genus common in the Pacific.

Pua kala **(E)**
Prickly Poppy

Argemone glauca
Family: Papaveraceae

Description

This wild, annual, native Hawaiian poppy grows to heights of about 4 feet, and many of its parts have a grayish appearance. The fruits and leaves are coarse and prickly. It flowers throughout much of the year. A center of yellowish-orange stamens and a dark red-tipped pistil add color to the white flower petals.

Distribution

Pua kala is endemic to Hawai'i, usually found in dry, rocky areas, generally in open woodlands. It seems to be most closely related to other poppy species in South America. Two varieties of this species are now recognized. The more common variety *Argemone glauca* var. *glauca* is found in dry woodlands from sea level to about 1,500 feet on the leeward sides of the high islands, except Kaua'i. *Argemone glauca* var. *decipiens*, with more prickles on its capsules is found only on Hawai'i Island in dry areas (2,000-6,000 feet).

Uses

Traditionally, Hawaiians have used the seeds and yellow sap of the fruit capsules for ulcers, toothache, and general neuralgia; the sap was also used to treat warts. Unlike the opium poppy (*Papaver somniferum*), *pua kala* contains no morphine or codeine.

'Ohai **(E)**
An Endangered Species
Sebania tomentosa
Family: Fabaceae

Description

This rare beach plant is a relatively low-lying, woody shrub. Its branches are silky and wool-covered. The compound leaves have a whitish tint that helps reflect some light and therefore protects the plant from harsh exposure to the intense solar radiation common in the Hawaiian shoreline environments. The orange or reddish flowers are about 1½ inches long. The flowering *'ohai* plant shown here (top right) belongs to a population found at 'Āpua Point on Hawai'i Island. The *'ohai* shown in the foreground of the photograph below belongs to a relict population found at Ka'ena Point on O'ahu.

Distribution

In the past, *'ohai* was fairly abundant in coastal environments. Today, unfortunately, it can only be found in very few places, and usually only in small numbers. In fact, residential and other development have seriously reduced its numbers, and it is now endangered even in remote areas . For example, in recent decades at Ka'ena Point area, the impact of motorcycling has damaged the small, threatened population that exists there. Small populations of *'ohai* can also still be found in some remote coastal areas such as Ka'alu'alu and 'Āpua Point on Hawai'i Island. Some people have successfully grown *'ohai* plants in home gardens. Flowers of *'ohai* bloom within six or seven months after germination. Those interested in cultivating native species should contact the Honolulu Botanical Gardens for information.

Ma'o, huluhulu **(E)**
Hawaiian Cotton
Gossypium tomentosum
Family: Malvaceae

Description

Ma'o or *huluhulu*, the native cotton plant, is a wide-branching shrub whose angular twigs are covered with a whitish down or hair. It is not a very tall shrub, rarely reaching more than two to six feet above the ground. The leaves of *ma'o* are 1½ to 2 inches in length and are divided into three or more lobes. The flowers have five yellow petals. Each of these is about ½ inch long and wrapped in a mass of white to brownish cotton fibers. Unlike some other cotton plants, *ma'o* has no structures beyond the flowers that produce nectar, or a sweet substance. It should be noted, that this character has been bred into certain commercial strains of upland cotton to make them less attractive to insects, which sometimes are vectors of cotton diseases.

Distribution

Ma'o occurs mostly in dry, rocky, or clay coastal plains, quite often very close to the ocean. It can be found on all of the main Hawaiian Islands, except the Big Island of Hawai'i. This native species of the cotton genus *Gossypium* is only found in the Hawaiian Islands and is therefore referred to as endemic. *Ma'o* is a wild relative of the American cottons of world commerce. Once more common along many arid coastlines and leeward lowlands of Hawai'i, today *ma'o* is rare in areas where the impact of urban and suburban development has disturbed its natural habitat. However, with adventurous perseverance and good fortune, one can still enjoy finding a small population of this unique native flowering plant. On the densely populated island of O'ahu, *ma'o* can be found in the dry coastal plain located between Makapu'u and Sandy Beach, as well as in the lowland area near Ka'ena Point.

'Iliahialo'e **(E)**
Beach Sandalwood
Santalum ellipticum var. *littorale*
Family: Santalaceae
Description

Native *'iliahialo'e* is a low shrub with succulent, gray-green, opposing leaves. Its tiny, yellowish-green flowers (four sepals) bloom in panicles at the leaf axils or branch tips. The green fruits turn red while ripening, but eventually become dark blue or black when fully mature.

Distribution

There are 25 species in the sandalwood genus *Santalum*. These are found in India, East Malaysia, Australia, and many Pacific islands. Hawai'i has four endemic species, found in coastal areas and the dry forests (*S. ellipticum*), in moderately wet forests (*S. freycinetianum*), in the sub-alpine zone on Haleakalā volcano of East Maui (*S. haleakalae*), or only on Hawai'i Island (*S. paniculatum*). *'Iliahialo'e* is found along some Hawaiian coasts. Some of the sandalwoods of Hawai'i may have evolved from a plant that grew from seeds that floated in, while others may have evolved from seeds that arrived originally in a bird's stomach.

Naio **(I)**
Bastard or False Sandalwood
Myoporum sandwicense
Family: Myoporaceae
Description

Naio can be found growing as a short shrub or moderately tall tree. The relatively thick, succulent leaves are narrow, fairly long, pointed, and arranged alternately. The whitish flowers are borne in axillary clusters and are about ½ inch wide. The whitish fruits are spherical, waxy, and about ¼ inch wide.

Distribution

Naio is indigenous in Hawai'i. This means that the species is native, but not unique to these islands. *Naio* grows from sea level up to about 8,000 feet elevation in the drier environments of Hawai'i. Among the numerous varieties of *naio*, those found near the coast that grow in thin or rocky soil tend to be rather small and shrubby.

Hawaiian *Nama* (E) *Nama sandwicensis* Family: Hydrophyllaceae

Description

Hawaiian *Nama* is a very small, low-lying, annual or short-lived perennial herb in the waterleaf family. Its only recorded Hawaiian name is *hinahina kahakai* (which is used on Ni'ihau). *Nama* forms small, prostrate clumps, usually less than 10 inches wide and rising only 1 to 2 inches above the ground. The leaves of this native plant are about 1½ inches long, inverted, and hairy. The small, attractive flowers have pale purple or pink petals with a yellowish central section.

Distribution

The mat-forming *Nama*, is endemic to Hawai'i. Thus, unlike most of the native coastal plants, this species is unique to the Hawaiian Archipelago. *Nama* is probably derived from an ancestral species in the tropical New World. It is still found on some coastal sand dunes, other sandy areas, or on raised limestone reefs of all the main Hawaiian islands except Kaho'olawe. *Nama* is also found on the small islands of Laysan and Lisianski, where the flowers are whitish, apparently because of a lost gene for petal color.

Hawaiian *Schiedea*
Schiedea globosa
Family: Caryophyllaceae

Description

Schiedea globosa has no known Hawaiian name. It is a small subshrub, only woody at its base and usually less than one foot tall. The smooth, succulent leaves are 1 to 3 inches long and pointed. Its stems are relatively large and jointed. Some plants in this species have only male flowers; others have only female flowers; and still others have bisexual flowers. This is a condition botanists sometimes refer to as half-way to dioecism. Dioecism refers to plants with separate male and female individuals, such as papaya (*Carica papaya*), true hemp or marijuana (*Cannabis sativa*), and the cycads.

Distribution

There are 22 species in the genus *Schiedea*, all of which are found only in Hawai'i and are thus referred to as endemic. They belong to the pink family, Caryophyllaceae. *Schiedea globosa,* shown here, can be found on steep, rocky slopes or cliffs along the southeastern coast of O'ahu where it grows in association with *nehe* (*Lipochaeta integrifolia*), *'ilima* (*Sila fallax*), and *koko* (*Chamaesyce degeneri*). It can also be found in similar habitats in some areas of Moloka'i and Maui. *Schiedea globosa*, like many other endemic native Hawaiian species (including others in the genus *Schiedea*), is quite rare and in need of protection.

Niu **(P)** *Cocos nucifera*
Coconut Palm Family: Arecaceae

Description

Reaching heights of 100 feet, coconut palms bear enormous leaves up to twenty feet in length with about 100 leaflets on each side of the palm frond midrib. After about ten years of growth, the coconut palm begins a continual bloom of flower clusters that lasts until it dies. In its earlier stages of development each cluster is surrounded by the green-colored spathe that eventually opens, progressively exposing numerous male flowers and sparingly few female flowers. The nuts of the coconut palm have a thick outer husk-like layer and hard thin inner shell layer. This structure encloses the edible, white, endosperm meat and milk. The coconut palm may live as long as seventy years or more.

Distribution

The coconut palm is found around the world in numerous tropical lowland and seashore environments which receive more than 30 to 40 inches of rainfall per year. Probably native to the Old World tropics, it is generally assumed that this extremely useful palm is not native to Hawai'i, but was originally introduced by Polynesian immigrants from the South Pacific.

Uses

The coconut palm is a marvelously diverse source of food, oil, fiber, and building material. It probably has more uses than any other plant known to man, with a very long cultural history as a major resource among Pacific Island peoples. In old Hawai'i, the trunk was carved out and used as a canoe or fashioned into the bodies of big drums. The long fronds or parts of them were used to make fans, brooms, and musical instruments. The fruit of the coconut also has many uses. Fibrous strands of the husk serve as kindling for fire and braiding material for cordage and rope. Coconut shells were used as drinking vessels, serving spoons, receptacles and small drums. As a food source, the milk and meat of the *niu* were forbidden for women.

Milo **(P)**
Portia Tree
Thespesia populnea
Family: Malvaceae

Description

Milo varies in size from a medium-sized shrub to an upright tree more than 20 feet tall with a dense crown. The shiny leaves are 3 to 5 inches wide and heart-shaped with a sharply tapering point. The attractive, yellowish flowers with purple centers tend to shrivel and turn purplish pink as the day progresses. They are 2 to 3 inches in diameter at their tips and can be seen blooming throughout much of the year. The fruits have 5 comparments and are borne in globular, woody capsules about an inch wide.

Distribution

Native to the Old World tropics, *milo* was probably brought to Hawai'i from the South Pacific by Polynesian immigrants many centuries ago (some botanists believe that this species may be indigenous to Hawai'i). Although one can frequently find *milo* growing along protected shores, it may have been more common in the past. Its buoyant, saltwater-resistant seeds have enabled it to disperse itself around the islands and become naturalized (established on its own) in many seaside locations.

Uses

Milo has long been used as a shade tree around Hawaiian seashore homes. The attractive, heavy, hardwood of *milo* is polished and made into bowls. The seeds of *milo* were taken as a laxative. The young leaves are said to be edible both in a raw or cooked condition, but the dry, globular fruits should not be eaten. On many tropical Pacific islands, the wood of this tree is used for firewood and building material, as well as to make paddles and handicraft products.

On the Hamakua Coast of Hawai'i Island with *'ōhi'a lehua*, *hala*, *naupaka kahakai*, and *ti* plant in the foreground, and ironwood, coconut palms and other species in the background.

Naupaka kahakai (*Scaevola taccada*, see page 9) on a sand dune at Ka'ena Point, O'ahu.

Hau **(I)** or **(P)**
Hibiscus tiliaceus
Family: Malvaceae

Description

Hau is a densely branching shrub or small tree up to 12 feet tall that may develop into an impenetrable thicket, especially along streams. The 2 to12 inch wide, heart-shaped leaves are large, rounded and leathery. Through the course of the day, the abundant, 2 to 3 inch long flowers of *hau* change color from yellow (left photo) to orange (opposite page) to red, eventually turning brownish and dropping to the ground. The inch-long fruiting capsule produces 3 seeds in each of its 5 valves.

Distribution

Polynesian immigrants probably brought cuttings of *hau* to Hawai'i and planted this useful species along the humid shores and inland on some lower mountain slopes. This very widespread species may also be indigenous to Hawai'i, arriving on its own before the first humans found Hawai'i. It is commonly found growing along many tropical Pacific beaches.

Uses

Hau is a very useful plant. In Old Hawai'i, the common people were strongly discouraged from harvesting any of its branches without chiefly permission. To regulate conservation of some marine sources, *hau* branches were periodically placed along the shore as a *kapu* sign indicating a time of restricted fishing. Materials made from parts of *hau* included fiber, net floats, canoe outriggers, and *kapa* cloth. Other plant parts were used for medical purposes.

***Kou* (P)** *Cordia subcordata*
Family: Boraginaceae

Description

Kou is a small but fast growing, erect, evergreen tree, rarely reaching heights of more than 30 feet tall, with a dense crown. The broad, smooth, pointed leaves are about 4 to 8 inches long and 3 to 5 inches wide. The flowers are attractive, about an inch long, tubular, and bright orange. The fruits are 1 to 2 inches long, clustered, contain 4 white seeds, and turn pale-grayish brown when mature.

Distribution

Kou is much less common in Hawai'i than it was before the arrival of Captain Cook in the late 18th century. Adapted to lowland areas including arid seashores, *kou* is not known to grow wild in Hawai'i. Probably native to insular Southeast Asia and many Western Pacific islands, it was introduced to the extremely isolated islands of Hawai'i by early Polynesian immigrants.

Uses

Kou has a very long history as an ornamental plant is eastern Africa, tropical Asia, tropical Australia, and several islands in the Pacific Ocean. In Old Hawai'i, it was one of the favorite shade trees and a valuable wood resource. It grows quickly and provides a light but strong, easily worked, beautiful wood for making prized utensils and religious statues. In addition, the leaves were reportedly used for coloring fishing lines, and the seeds were sometimes eaten.

***Pohāpohā* (R)**
Love-in-a-Mist, Running Pop
Passiflora foetida
Family: Passifloraceae

Description

Pohāpohā is a passion fruit vine with hairy leaves that commonly have 3 lobes. Tendrils grow out of the leaf axils located between the stems and the leaf stalks. Its flowers are whitish, about 1½ inches wide, and produce large, lacy bracts that cover the buds and fruit. The smooth, red fruits are about ¾ of an inch in diameter.

Distribution

Like most of the 400 or more passion fruit species (in the genus *Passiflora*), this one is native to tropical America. There are no native Hawaiian passion fruit plants; all the 10 or more species now found growing wild (naturalized) in Hawai'i were introduced after the arrival of Captain Cook (1778). Even the yellow-fruited, tasty *liliko'i* (*Passiflora edulis*) is a relatively recent arrival in Hawai'i. Many of the alien passion fruit plants have escaped cultivation. Some of these wild introduced species have become significant pests, especially in the native forest areas of Hawai'i (e.g., *Passiflora mollissima*, banana poka). Alien *pohāpohā* vines grow over rocky areas and other shrubs in the drier coastal areas of Hawai'i.

Alena, nena **(I)** *Boerhavia* spp.

Description Family: Nyctaginaceae

Plants known as *alena* (or *nena*) in Hawai'i are small, low-lying perennials that spread out over the ground. Slender to roundish leaves, up to about 1½ inches in length, are produced mainly on the lower half of the plant. Flowers are white or pinkish, quite small, and tubular. They are produced at the end of thin stalks which are a few inches long.

Distribution

Three native species of *Boerhavia* are found in Hawai'i, but less commonly than in the past. Two of these species, *B. glabrata* and *B. repens,* are indigenous in Hawai'i, and one, *B. herbstii*, is endemic. Because their sticky fruits adhere easily to seabirds and shorebirds, some *alena* species occur on or near sandy seashores of many tropical Pacific islands. There is also one alien *Boerhavia* species in Hawai'i.

Uses

Traditionally Hawaiians have used the large roots of some *alena* plants for medicinal purposes. The leaves may be eaten if cooked properly; however, beware: over consumption can harm your kidneys!

Nanea (I) Vigna marina
Beach Pea Family: Fabaceae

Description

The beach pea, has several Hawaiian names, such as *nanea, mohihihi, lemuomakili, nenea, 'ōkolemakili, pūhili,* and *wahine 'ōma'o*. It is a low-lying, spreading, somewhat succulent vine with a more or less woody base. Its stems are often long, extending many feet along the ground, or climbing up over lower vegetation. The thick, light green leaves are each divided into three oval-shaped leaflets about three inches long. The flowers of this native beach pea are about ½ inch wide and bright yellow. The seedpods are about 2 inches long and about ¼ inch in width. Individual pods enclose 4 to 9 brownish seeds.

Distribution

The beach pea is an indigenous species in many tropical areas of the world, including Hawai'i. It grows along the seashore, where it tolerates intense solar radiation, strong winds, and frequent salt-spray. Unlike the Indian, Fijian and other tropical Pacific Island varieties of this species, the Hawaiian beach pea tends to develop thicker leaves and a more tightly packed form of growth. It is often found in association with *pōhuehue* and *naupaka kahakai.*

Uses

Although it is basically a native plant able to propagate without human help, the beach pea is sometimes cultivated in the yards of coastal homes because of its value as a ground cover and the attractiveness of its yellow flowers and shiny leaves. On some tropical Pacific Islands, parts of this plant are used traditionally for medicinal purposes.

Waina kahakai **(R)**
Sea grape, beach grape
Coccoloba uvifera
Family: Polygonaceae

Description

This ornamental tree produces a contorted, but smooth-barked trunk that may grow to be as much as 3 feet thick and over 20 feet high. Its gnarled branches and large, round, glossy leaves form a dense canopy. The broad leaves, which sometimes grow to be more than a half a foot in width, have yellow to reddish colored veins. The tiny, sweet-smelling flowers are produced on a spike several inches long, and the ½ inch wide green fruit, that become dark in color when ripe, hang in clusters.

Distribution

Although this tree has a Hawaiian name, it is native to tropical America and was introduced in Hawai'i in relatively recent times to serve as an ornamental plant and windbreak along our shores and in lowland environments. It can be cultivated from both seeds and cuttings. The sea grape grows well in almost pure sand. However, when planted inland, it is often attacked by insects. Although it produces fruit abundantly, no self-sown seedlings have been recorded for this tree in Hawai'i.

Uses

The sea or beach grape is known to some as an "autograph" tree because marks on fresh leaves produce clear white lines. Jelly and a liquor-like drink can be made from the fruit, and the astringent roots can be used medicinally for dysentery problems. The wood can be used for fuel, furniture construction, and as a boiled source of reddish dye. In addition, the bark gum is applied in tanning procedures and used as a medicine for sore throats.

Indian pluchea, Indian fleabane (R)

Pluchea indica
Family: Asteraceae

Description

Indian pluchea is a densely-branched, shrub species which may grow to heights of 5 feet. The tough, alternating leaves are about 1½ inches long and have a few "teeth" on their margins. Its pink or purple flowers are clustered at the branch ends. Tufts of light-colored hair are attached to each fruit and serve as a means for wind-borne dispersal. A close relative, *Pluchea carolinensis*, known as "sourbush," is also found in Hawai'i. It has densely matted, tiny hairs on the lower leaf surfaces. In addition, a sprawling hybrid, *Pluchea* x *fosbergii*, occurs wherever Indian pluchea and sourbush grow together.

Distribution

These weedy, alien *Pluchea* species are members of the aster or sunflower family. They are native to southeastern Asia, and only arrived in Hawai'i recently. Here, these plants occur on or near the coasts, on coral beaches, along the margins of salt marshes, and are especially widespread in waste areas and empty lots near coastal areas.

Golden crown-beard (R)
Verbesina encelioides
Family: Asteraceae
Description

This upright-growing, alien plant attains heights of up to 4 or 5 feet but usually is not more than about 2 feet tall at maturity. It has rather narrow, serrated leaves with small hairs on the upper sides. Like many members of the extremely large sunflower or aster family, the flowering heads (capitula) of this plant have an attractive color. The flowers are about 1 to 2 inches wide and are composed of many central disc florets with about a dozen petal-like ray flowers along the outer margins.

Distribution

Golden crown-beard is an annual, weedy herb. It is native to the warm and southern regions of the continental United States and northern Mexico. In Hawai'i, this introduced species is commonly found in disturbed or waste areas that are arid and close to the seashore. It occurs on all of the main islands except Ni'ihau, and on atolls of Kure and Midway in the Northwest Hawaiian Islands. In the springtime, one can sometimes see fields of yellow-colored golden crown-beard along the roadsides of some coastal environments. Unfortunately, on Green Island (Kure Atoll), this aggressive alien annual herb grows so densely that it has adversely affected seabird nesting in that ferderally protected national wildlife area.

Chinese violet,
Coromandel (R)

Asystasia gangetica
Family: Acanthaceae

Description

This weedy species of *Asystasia*, known as chinese violet or coromandel, is a trailing or climbing, perennial herb with stems 1½ to 6 feet long. It produces opposing leaves 1 to 4 inches long. The attractive violet or whitish flowers are grouped in clusters of 6 to 10. Each flower is about an inch in length with spreading lobes.

Distribution

In Hawai'i, chinese violet is an alien species (sometimes referred to as an introduced or exotic plant). This species was probably brought to the Hawaiian Islands by humans in relatively recent times. It has often escaped from cultivation in gardens and now grows wild in disturbed or open environments along the coasts and lowlands of Midway Atoll, Kaua'i, O'ahu, Moloka'i, and Maui. In many places, chinese violet spreads up fences and over other plants to heights several feet above ground. The wide native range of this species includes parts of tropical India, the Malay Peninsula and Africa.

ʻĀkulikuli kai **(R)**
Pickleweed, saltwort
Batis maritima
Family: Bataceae

Description

ʻĀkulikuli kai is a small shrub with woody stems. Its leaves are smooth, fleshy, and cylindrical. The common English name for this plant, pickleweed, was inspired by the pickle-like odor of the salty juice produced in its succulent leaves. The flowers of the pickleweed are very small and yellowish-green. They are clustered on small spikes growing out from the branch tips or leaf axils. Pickleweed is a dioecious plant; therefore, the male and female flowers are found on separate plants.

Distribution

ʻĀkulikuli kai, or pickleweed, is an alien species that was introduced into the Hawaiian Islands well over 100 years ago. It is a salt-tolerant plant that can now be found growing in large clumps along many marshy shorelines, coastal estuaries, and ponds in Hawaiʻi. It has extensively invaded many of the traditional Hawaiian fishponds, which are located along the coasts of the islands.

Uses

According to Marie Neal, the succulent leaves of the pickleweed are edible and can be used in salads. In addition, pickleweed leaves are said to have medicinal value. In the Caribbean region, pickleweed ash is used in the production of soap and glass products.

***ʻĀkulikuli* (I)**
Sea purslane

Sesuvium portulacastrum
Family: Aizoaceae

Description

This native *ʻākulikuli* plant is a low-lying or prostrate herb with trailing branches and fleshy stems. Its narrow succulent leaves are about 1½ inches long. The attractive, white to magenta, five-parted flowers are borne at the leaf axils.

Distribution

Sesuvium portulacastrum is an indigenous herb distributed widely and native in many tropical coastal regions. As a salt-tolerant or halophytic plant, it can be found near the beach, alongside brackish marshlands, or surrounding the shores of sandy lagoons. It is also commonly encountered along various sandy or rocky beaches of Hawaiʻi.

Uses

It is said that the fleshy parts of *Sesuvium portulacastrum* are edible, and may be eaten either raw or cooked as greens. However, one should always be cautious when collecting wild plants for food. Know your species well! To eliminate the salty taste of this *ʻākulikuli*, the water should be drained and replaced a few times when cooking parts of the plant.

Tree heliotrope (R)
Tournefortia argentea
Family: Boraginaceae

Description

The tree heliotrope rarely grows to heights of more than 20 feet. It usually has a rounded canopy of long, broad, hairy, pale-colored leaves clustered at the branch tips. Like other species in Boraginaceae, the heliotrope family, the flowers of the tree heliotrope have five parts. These are small, bell-shaped, and clustered on coiled spikes. Its fruit are small, round, fleshy, and white when ripe.

Distribution

The tree heliotrope is commonly found along tropical sandy beaches in many regions of the Indian and Pacific Oceans where it is an indigenous species. However, in Hawai'i it is an alien plant that was introduced along the seashore environments of Hawai'i in the 19th century. Today it is planted as an ornamental in yards of beach houses and naturalized in some coastal areas of Hawai'i.

Uses

In India, the leaves of this heliotrope tree are eaten by some people because of their flavor that supposedly resembles parsley. In the mythology of the Polynesians living in the Tuamotu atolls of the South Pacific, the tree heliotrope is said to be among the first living things to be created in the world. The leaves and other parts of the plant have important medicinal value on many tropical Pacific islands.

***Nena, kīpūkai, hinahina* (I)** *Heliotropium curassavicum*
Seaside heliotrope Family: Boraginaceae

Description

The seaside heliotrope is a small, low-lying, annual herb with trailing stems 4 to 15 inches long. The pale green leaves are narrow, succulent, and about 1 inch long. The tiny, whitish flowers are borne in coiled clusters referred to by botanists as scorpioid cymes.

Distribution

The native seaside heliotrope is considered to be an indigenous, not endemic, Hawaiian plant. In other words, it is also a native plant elsewhere in the world, under generally similar ecological conditions, and was spread to the Hawaiian Islands without human assistance, probably long before the arrival of the first Polynesian immigrants. The seaside heliotrope is a halophyte (salt-tolerant species) found growing in clay soils near the shore. Since the seeds do not float, it has been suggested that birds carry the seeds of the plant from island to island in small clay clods attached to their feet.

Uses

Ancient Hawaiians are said to have used the succulent leaves of the seaside heliotrope in the brewing of a therapeutic beverage.

Noni **(P)**
Indian mulberry

Morinda citrifolia
Family: Rubiaceae

Description

Noni is a short evergreen tree or shrub. It has large, broad, opposing leaves 6 to 10 inches long that are thick and shiny. The flowers are whitish, about a 1/3 of an inch long, and clustered into rounded heads that develop into a yellow to green fruits 2 to 4 inches long.

Distribution

Although it may be an indigenous species in Hawai'i, many believe that *noni* was brought to these islands from some South Pacific island by ancient Polynesian immigrants. It can be found growing wild along several rocky, lava-strewn, coastal environments of Hawai'i. It is also cultivated in some lowland gardens and farms on these islands.

Uses

Noni is one of the most important traditional medicinal plants of the Pacific Islanders, long used for many therapeutic applications. Its use as a natural cure-all has, in recent years, made it widely popular in various areas beyond the Pacific. Its rather foul-smelling, edible fruit was probably used as a famine food in the past. A yellowish dye can be made from the stem bark; and a red dye can be made from the root bark.

False *kamani, kamani haole* (R)
Tropical or Indian almond
Terminalia catappa
Family: Combretaceae

Description

This tropical evergreen tree can develop into a large seashore plant as tall as 50 feet or more. It produces expansive, horizontally oriented branches with large, broad, rounded leaves several inches wide that turn red before dropping off. The spikes of small white flowers produce smooth, tough, flattened fruits about 2 inches long when mature with ridged edges and relatively small kernels.

Distribution

False *kamani* is native to insular Southeast Asia, and possibly on some Western Pacific islands. It is now a common tree along sandy shorelines in many tropical regions including Hawai'i where it was introduced after the arrival of Captain Cook (the useful, but now relatively rare, "true" *kamani* tree, *Calophyllum inophyllum*, was brought to Hawai'i by early Polynesian immigrants). The false *kamani* is naturalized along many Hawaiian beaches, growing close to the shore. Like many trees adapted to coastal environments, the false *kamani* fruits can float and tolerate seawater for some time. Therefore, its fruits can be dispersed from one beach to another by ocean currents.

Uses

A popular ornamental plant, the false *kamani* serves as shade tree, a source of useable timber, a plant with medicinal properties, and a dye source. In addition, the fruits contain an edible seed that has an excellent flavor but takes considerable effort to extract.

Koali 'awa, koali, 'awahia **(I)**
Morning Glory
Ipomoea indica
Family: Convolvulaceae

Distribution

Worldwide, in subtropical and tropical regions, there are about 500 morning glory species in the genus *Ipomoea*. Several of these have been introduced into Hawai'i. Many have escaped from cultivation and are now naturalized as weedy plants found in various environments from the forests down to the seashore. The species shown here is a common, widespread species that is indigenous to Hawai'i, where it is found in lowland, dry, disturbed areas. Known in Hawaiian as *koali 'awa*, *koali*, *'awahia*, *koali lā'au* (on Ni'ihau), and *koali pehu*, it can be seen growing in some areas as a trailing vine covering rocky areas not far from the shoreline. Hawaiians have long used the roots, leaves, and seeds of this species for medicinal purposes.

Australian saltbush (R)
Atriplex semibaccata
Family: Chenopodiaceae

Description

The Australian saltbush is a densely branching, low-lying herb. Alone, it may cover an area as much as ten to twenty feet in diameter. The leaves are about ½ to 2 inches in length and have grayish hairs. The male and female flowers are separate but are produced on the same plant, and like other members of Chenopodiaceae (the goosefoot or pigweed family), the flowers are very small and lack petals. Probably the most noticeable feature of this small plant is its reddish, fleshy, fruiting bract. The seeds are borne in between a pair of mature bracts.

Distribution

Native to Australia, where it has been a valuable item in the grazing diet of sheep, this alien plant is said to have been brought to Lāna‘i in 1895 for forage use. The small seeds of the saltbush are be dispersed by both wind and ocean currents. It has become widely naturalized in Hawai‘i and can now be found on many islands in arid or salty soils, usually near the coast. Below, a clump of the Australian saltbush is shown on raised coral limestone located along the Wai‘anae coast of O‘ahu.

***Lilia lana i ka wai* (R)**
Water Lily
Nymphaea spp.
Family: Nymphaeaceae

Description

Water lilies are not true members of the lily family (Liliaceae), but they are among the most beautiful of all aquatic plants (see page 2). The water lilies grown in Hawaiian pools and ponds have red, pink, blue, lavender, yellow, and white flowers; they are cup-shaped, have many petals, and may measure several inches in diameter. The large, floating leaves of the water lilies are rounded, leathery, and are usually cut deeply at the base. Long stems attach the leaves to the roots that are embedded in the mud under a few inches to several feet of water.

Distribution and Uses

As popular aquatic plants, various water lilies are often cultivated in ponds near the Hawaiian coastlines. Alien to the islands of Hawai‘i, they were introduced for ornamental purposes. Some water lilies have had sacred associations in ancient Egypt, Greece, and the Orient. In some cultures, the beautiful flowering bloom of these plants are seen as the emergence of purity and regeneration, arising from a muddy birthplace, up through, and eventually above the water to shine brilliantly in the sun. To some, water lilies represent a symbolic resurrection or transcendental awakening, while others cook and eat the seeds and parts of the rootstock. Still others grow the plant for strictly ornamental purposes.

Nua‘ailua Bay and Ke‘anae Peninsula on the windward coast of East Maui

Brackish water pond, Luahine-wai, near Kīhono, Kona, Hawai'i. Plants surrounding the pond include *niu* (coconut palm), *kiawe* trees, *milo*, and alien grasses

Aerial view of Southeast, O'ahu

Red or American Mangrove (R)
Rhizophora mangle
Family: Rhizophoraceae

Description

This alien tree has a rounded crown, a dense branching system, and aerial or stilt roots. The leaves grow to about 6 inches in length, have smooth margins, and are arranged opposite each other. The flowers are produced on relatively long stems. They are about an inch wide and have 4 prominent yellowish sepals. The fruits, about an inch long, are viviparous. In other words, the rather unusual fruits of the mangrove germinate while they are still attached to the parent plant. Eventually each germinated fruit, up to a foot in length, drops into the surrounding mud or surf; and at high tide it may be swept away.

Distribution

The red mangrove is native to tropical America and western Polynesia, and only relatively recently was it brought to Hawai'i by humans. In fact, it was introduced into the mudflat environments of Hawai'i in 1902, and has since spread into many marshy places and along stream banks near the sea. In some areas, of our islands such as parts of Pearl Harbor, on O'ahu, mangrove thickets have increased their distribution significantly during this century.

Uses

Mangrove forests, in their native habitats, are said to be advantageous because of their dense growth, and because their aerial roots trap sediments, which they hold together and thus extend the land area. However, these alien plants are presently choking the traditional Hawaiian fishponds and are extremely difficult to remove once established. In parts of tropical America the leaves and bark of the red mangrove are used as a source of tannin for curing leather; the dense, dark wood is also used as a source of fuel and building material; and the bark and shoots can be used to produce a dye.

***Ali'ipoe, li'ipoe, poloka* (R)** *Canna indica*
Canna, Indian shot Family: Cannaceae

Description

Canna is a tall, alien, perennial herb with leafy, flowering stems. It may grow to heights of 3 feet or more from a large swollen underground stem. The long leaves are oval and narrow. The flowers are reddish (the hybrids of *Canna* x *generalis* produce yellow and speckled flowers). The black seeds are produced in erect, rugged seed cases about 1 inch long.

Distribution

Canna was introduced as an ornamental plant to Hawai'i in relatively recent times. Since then it has escaped from gardens to become rather widespread in the humid lowland environments of the Hawaiian Islands. It can form large thickets; and occasionally it can be found naturalized along the margins of marshes or brackish water ponds. It is native to tropical America and was brought to Hawai'i sometime after the arrival of Captain Cook in 1778.

Uses

Hawaiian *lei* makers occasionally use the attractive, very dark brown to black seeds of canna plants. In Hawai'i these seeds are referred to as *li'ipoe*. The hard seeds are also sometimes used as rattle noisemakers, placed inside *la'amia*, the introduced calabash fruit (*Crescentia cujete*).

Paina (R)
Ironwood, beefwood, she-oak
Casuarina equisetifolia
Family: Casuarinaceae

Description

This very dense, hardwood tree is a fast growing woody plant. It may grow to heights of 80 feet within 10 years of germination or cloning by planting a stem cutting. The bark is light to dark gray, and the trunk wood is very tough and dark red in color. Ironwood does not have true leaves. Its "needles" are actually thread-shaped, jointed, greenish branchlets. Look for the tiny, brownish, teeth-like organs at each branchlet joint. These are vestigial leaves. During May and June, male and female flowers are borne separately. The small male flowers form brownish cylinder-like tips at the ends of some branchlets. The small female flowers form red clusters at the base of the branchlets. The cone-like fruits are about ½ inch long and brown when ripe.

Distribution

Native to Northern Australia, this ironwood species has been introduced within the last two hundred years to many tropical Pacific islands, including Hawai'i. It is now widely naturalized throughout these islands, especially in drier, poor soil environments. Here it is found from sea level up to above 3,000 feet.

Uses

In many more or less arid, eroded areas, ironwood has been planted as a rapid growing tree for watershed protection. Although it is used as an effective windbreak, a soil or sand binder, and an aid in nitrogen fixation in the soil, in many areas it often grows into thick stands that virtually choke out the growth of practically every other kind of plant. Some refer to those forest groves that are heavily dominated ironwood trees as "biological deserts." The extremely tough roots of ironwood also break up some paved areas. In other islands of the Pacific region, where this tree was first introduced by early Pacific Islanders, the dense wood was carved into tough war clubs, and the therapeutic inner bark is still used to soothe sore throats and other ailments.

***Kiawe, Keawe* (R)**
Algaroba, mesquite
Prosopis pallida
Family: Fabaceae

Description

Kiawe, a medium-sized tree in the bean family, can grow to heights of over 50 feet. Variable in size and form, it develops very deep root systems that tap the ground water in dry areas. The trunk and branches are twisted and the crown is large and wide-spread. The leaves are compound, each containing dozens of small leaflets. The tiny yellow flowers are borne on long, cylindrical spikes, usually during the spring; and the fruit are stiff, yellowish, and waxy.

Distribution

A native of South America (Peru, Colombia, and Ecuador), *kiawe* and its close relatives are widespread in the New World. Today, this alien tree is a dominant part of the dry, lowland regions of the main islands of Hawai'i. Common near sandy shores and in the arid plains in Hawai'i, it is also found on the drier slopes up to almost 2,000 ft. Beware of its long thorns!

Uses

In 1828, Father Bachelot first imported seeds of this tree from the Royal Gardens in Paris. A single cultivated tree grown from one of these seeds on the Catholic Mission ground on Fort Street, Honolulu is said to have become the ancestor of all other *kiawe* trees in Hawai'i! Infact, this alien tree is now very common and useful in Hawai'i. It provides fuelwood, a tasty honey, nutritious pods for pig and cattle feed, and is used as a reforestation tree in the lower, dry forests. However, its very deep roots may lower water tables in coastal regions.

***Koa haole, ēkoa* (R)**
Leucaena leucocephala
Family: Fabaceae

Description

Koa haole is a shrub or small tree that reaches heights up to about 30 feet. Standing upright, it produces globular, white, flower heads roughly an inch in diameter. It has compound leaves and bunches of long, thin, brown pods that enclose numerous small brown seeds.

Distribution

Koa haole is native to tropical America but has been spread by humans to many other tropical areas of the world. It was introduced into the Hawaiian lowlands and dry forests early in the 19th century. It is a prime example of an alien species that has successfully invaded very extensive areas in Hawai'i, especially near the coast and on the lower arid slopes. Its relatively deep tap roots make it difficult to remove from those areas where it has become well established.

Uses

In Hawai'i, *koa haole* has served as cattle feed, firewood, erosion control, soil improvement, and the seeds are strung into *lei*s. In addition, botanists have noted that stands of *koa haole* offer shade for natural regeneration of native species, and as a legume, it acts as a host for nitrogen fixing bacteria that attach themselves to the roots. Thus it has been called a "nurse crop." Nevertheless, it has become an aggressive, dominant pest in many areas.

***Lākana, lā'au kalakala, lanakana (Ni'ihau), mikinolia hihiu, mikinoli hohono, mikinoli kukū* (R)**

Lantana

Lantana camara

Family: Verbanaceae

Description

This thorny shrub usually grows to heights of 3 to 6 feet, but can grow as high as 15 feet or more. Clustered into compact heads, the small tubular flowers vary in color including yellow, orange, white, pink, and red. Hikers will recognize the attractive flowers and the pungent smell of this plant, but will find it very troublesome to move through its dense, prickly growth.

Distribution

A native of tropical America, lantana covers over exposed areas from sea level up to about 3,000 feet in moist as well as dry habitats. It was introduced into Hawai'i as an ornamental plant in 1858. Since then, lantana has become a severe pest in several places in these islands. Spread by berry-feeding birds, lantana is now one of the most common, invasive, weedy plants in many tropical areas of the world!

'Ihi **(I)**
Portulaca lutea [photo above]
Family: Portulacaceae

Pigweed, *'ākulikuli kula, 'ākulikuli lau li'i, 'ihi* **(R)**
Portulaca oleracea [photo below]
Family: Portulacaceae

Descriptions: The native and introduced species known in Hawaiian as *'ihi* (or by other names for the alien *Portulaca oleracea*, see above) are small, low lying, perennial or annual herbs. They have relatively thick, fleshy brown or reddish-green branches. The leaves are generally less than an inch long and succulent. The small, bright-yellow flowers are about ¼ of an inch wide, and the seeds are quite tiny.

Distribution

There are seven species of *Portulaca* in Hawai'i, one indigenous, three endemic, and three naturalized aliens. The most common native species, *P. lutea*, is indigenous, commonly found near seashores of many tropical Pacific Islands. In Hawai'i, it is generally rare on the main islands, but can be found in relative abundance is some regions of these high islands and on many of our northwestern islands. Pigweed (*P. oleracea*) is the most common introduced *Portulaca* species. This close relative of the native *'ihi* species is a very widespread, weedy plant that is sometimes used as a pot herb. It is naturalized in many parts of the world including the lowlands of Hawai'i, and it usually lies closer to the ground than the native *'ihi* plants.

***ʻŌhiʻa ma ka nahele* (R)**
Cherry Tomato
Solanum lycopersicum var. *cerasiforme*
Family: Solanaceae

The cherry tomato grows weedy or wild in Hawaiʻi as a low, shrubby, hairy plant in some exposed areas from sea level up to 1,000 feet or more in elevation. The leaves of the cherry tomato are divided into pointed, toothed leaflets. The flowers are about three-quarters of an inch wide, yellowish, and are produced in clusters. The edible fruits are approximately ½ to ¾ of an inch wide and bright red. The cherry tomato is a member of a large family known variously as the tomato, potato, or nightshade family. It is an alien species in Hawaiʻi. The native home range of the cherry tomato is in Peru and Ecuador. It was introduced to the Hawaiian Islands by humans more than 100 years ago and is now dispersed to various relatively low-lying, open or disturbed sites on all the main islands by birds and other animals. It is also often cultivated for its tasty and decorative fruit. The species name of tomato, a major world crop, is *Solanum lycopersicum*. The cherry tomato is a wild growing variety of this species. It produces smaller fruits than cultivated tomato plants.

'Emoloa, kāwelu, kalamālō
Eragrostis variabilis
Family: Poaceae

Description and Distribution

One of the largest and most important families of flowering plants is the grass family (Poaceae). It includes approximately 600 genera and about 10,000 annual and perennial species. This family is extremely widespread and includes major crop plants such as wheat, oats, barley, sugar cane, sorghum, millet, maize (corn), and rice. Hawai'i has many wild species of grasses. Of these, 39 are endemic, 8 are indigenous, and more than100 are alien. Only a few grass species found near the seashore in Hawai'i are shown here. The top left photograph on this page shows *Eragrostis variabilis*, an endemic, perennial grass species known as *'emoloa, kāwelu,* or *kalamālō*. Reaching heights of about 20 to 40 inches, it is found on sand dunes, grasslands, open dry forest sites, several of the Northwestern Hawaiian Islands, and all the main islands.

Fountain grass (R)
Pennisetum setaceum
Family: Poaceae

Description and Distribution

Fountain grass, a perennial species, produces non-branching, bunched stems up to about 3 feet in height. The curved leaf blades are rough, relatively narrow, and 1 to 2 feet long. The feathery, flowering panicles are cylindrical, pink to purple, and 6 to 14 inches in length. Fountain grass is native to Africa, and like many other introduced species, including several grasses, it has escaped from ornamental gardens and naturalized itself in a number of areas in the Hawaiian Islands. This species is now considered to be a very serious pest in Hawai'i. It is an aggressive colonizer of arid, open places, often out-competing native species. It is also strongly adapted to fires, re-establishing itself very quickly after a burn. In fact, its dense, dry vegetative growth burns fast and hot, inflicting widespread damage to the remaining, and largely threatened or endangered, native dry forest species.

Swollen Fingergrass (*Chloris barbata*, Family: Poaceae, see above) is known as *mau'u lei*. It is an alien species in Hawai'i that is found in drier, disturbed areas, often near sea level.

'Aki'aki (*Sporobolus virginicus*, Family: Poaceae, see below) is indigenous to Hawai'i. It has a worldwide distribution in warm coastal areas where it is found near the high-tide line.

ʻŪlei, eluehe (Molokaʻi), ***u ʻulei*** **(E)**
Osteomeles anthyllidifolia
Family: Rosaceae

Description

ʻŪlei is an evergreen shrub that grows relatively close to the ground. The leaves consist of several pairs of opposing leaflets and one leaflet at the tip. The white, rose-like flowers are about 1/2 an inch wide and have five petals. The round, white fruits are about 1/3 of an inch wide.

Distribution

Native to Hawaiʻi, *ʻūlei* can be found growing from sea level up to several thousand feet in the drier areas of the Hawaiian Islands.

Uses

In ancient Hawaiʻi, *ʻūlei* wood was used to make digging sticks, fish spears, and *ʻūkēkē*, a native type of musical bow having two or three strings that were strummed. The orange-colored vine growing over the *ʻūlei* plant shown in the photograph below is *kaunaʻoa* (*Cuscuta sandwichiana*), an endemic member of the dodder family (Cuscutaceae). This native parasite absorbs nourishing substances from a host plant. It is superficially quite similar to another parasitic plant (*Cassytha filiformis*), also known as *kauna'oa*, in the laurel family (Lauraceae), that commonly grows over the ground or vegetation on or near the shores of many tropical Pacific Islands.

A late afternoon rainbow near the coast at Kaupō, Maui

On the east coast of Hawai'i Island, the afternoon sun highlights the wild grasses, including Natal redtop grass, *Melinis repens*, an alien species native to Africa, now common in Hawai'i.

***Wiliwili* (E)**
Erythrina sandwicensis
Family: Fabaceae

Description

Wiliwili trees are about 15 to 45 feet tall, with short, thick, twisted, somewhat thorny trunks. The ovate leaflets are 2 to 3 inches wide and drop off in the summer, helping avoid desiccation. The flowers are red, white, yellowish, or orange. The hanging, slightly constricted pods hold about 1 to 3 red to yellowish orange seeds.

Distribution

Wiliwili is endemic to Hawai'i, and much less common today than in the past. It is said to be very closely related to *Erythrina tahitensis* (endemic to Tahiti) and *E. velutina* (widespread in northern South America and some Caribbean Islands). *Wiliwili* can be found growing from near sea level, up to about 2,000 feet, especially in dry leeward forests and grassy slopes on all the main islands.

Uses

Its seeds can be strung into *lei,* and its light, soft wood was used to make surfboards, canoe outriggers, and fishnet floats. An old proverb suggests that sharks bite (take bait) when the *wiliwili* flowers.

'Ōhi'a lehua (E)
Metrosideros polymorpha
Family: Myrtaceae

Description

This attractive native plant is probably the most abundant of all Hawaiian trees. Diverse in size and shape, one can find very small, naturally stunted forms in the wet bogs, on new lava flows, and dry cliffs, as well as 80 ft. giants growing in the fertile soils of some forests. Size, shape, and surface features of the leaves differ from tree to tree as well as from region to region. The attractive reddish (or occasionally yellowish) flowers contain many stamens (male organ) and one pistil (felmale organ).

Distribution

Endemic *'ōhi'a lehua* trees occupy many types of environments from near sea level (see also top photograph on page 29) to over 8,000 ft. elevation.

Uses

The dark, hard, and long-lasting *'ōhi'a* wood was used in canoe making, house building, and the production of poi boards, bowls, and temple statues. Traditionally, young reddish -crisom leaves *(liko lehua)* and the flowers have been used for medicinal purposes.

***Maiapilo, pilo, pua pilo* (E)**

Native caper bush

Capparis sandwichiana

Family: Capparaceae

Description

Maiapilo is a shrub with 3 to 15 foot long, straggling stems. The leaves are fleshy, light green, oblong, and about 1 to 2½ inches long. The flowers open after sunset. Their 4 white petals turn pink with age, and surround a delicate mass of long stamens. The night-blooming flowers fade soon after daylight. The Hawaiian names for this plant refer to the strong, perfumed flower odor or to the rather unpleasant smell of its fruit pulp. The green, oblong, ridged fruits are about 2 inches long.

Distribution

Found on all the main Hawaiian Islands, and some smaller ones, *maiapilo* is less common than it was in the past. *Maiapilo* grows on coral, basaltic lava rock, and soil along the coast or somewhat inland, usually less than 300 feet above sea level. It is very similar to *Capparis cordifolia*, which is widespread in the Pacific. Heidi Bornhorst, author of a native plant cultivation book, is shown below.

Uses

Many people are familiar with capers, the pickled flower buds of *Capparis spinosa, a close* relative of *Maiapilo. Capparis sandwichiana* has traditional medicinal value.

***ʻĀkia, kauhi* (E)**

Wistroemia spp.
Family: Thymelaeaceae

Description and Distribution

Wikstroemia is a genus of about 50 species of shrubs and small trees found in areas of Southeast Asia, Australia and the Pacific. Twelve of these species are endemic to the Hawaiian Islands. The small, yellowish flowers of these unique Hawaiian species are very similar. However, the size, texture, and color of the leaves of plants belonging to even a single species often differ depending upon environmental factors such as elevation, habitat, and season. The small fruits range in color from orange to red to crimson. Shown here is *Wikstroemia uva-ursi,* a densely branching, low-lying, often sprawling shrub up to about 5 feet in height. Commonly cultivated, it is found in a variety of environments, including coastal areas on Kauaʻi, Oʻahu, Molokaʻi, and Maui.

Uses

Wikstroemia spp. provided a strong fiber for making ropes in Hawaiʻi. In the past, parts of the plant were said to have been used as poisons to stun and catch fish, and to execute criminals.

'Ena'ena, pūheu (Ni`ihau) **(E)**
Native cudweed, everlasting
Pseudonaphalium sandwicensium
Family: Asteraceae

Description

'Ena 'ena is a native perennial herb that forms a sprawling mat as it grows over the ground. It forms few to many branches and is moderately to very densely covered with tiny hairs. The leaves are about 1 inch wide and ½ to 2½ inches long. The small flowering heads of this member of the sunflower or daisy family produce bracts that are whitish to pale yellow when in bloom.

Distribution

Pseudonaphalium sandwicensium (*'ena 'ena*) is closely related to, and formerly classifed in the large, widespread genus *Gnaphalium* (sunflower family), which contains about 200 species. Since *'ena 'ena* is only found in the Hawaiian Islands, biologists refer to it as being endemic, or being unique to a particular area. It is found in moderately dry areas growing in clay or consolidated (lithified or cemented) sand dunes near sea level (the photographs here were taken near the shore at Mo'omomi, Moloka'i). It also occurs in higher regions of Hawai'i, up to about 9,000 feet elevation, especially on lava or cinders. *'Ena'ena* has been reported from all of the main Hawaiian islands (except Kaho'olawe) and Kure and Midway atolls.

Pōpolo, ʻākia (Niʻihau) **(E)** *Solanum nelsonii*
Family: Solanaceae

Description

Pōpolo is a low-lying or sprawling shrub up to about 3 feet tall. Its young stems and leaves are covered with many, tiny, multiple-branching hairs. The grayish green leaves are about 1½ inches long and 1 inch wide. They are arranged alternately along the stems. The small flowers are white with a tinge of lavender to pale purple. The small berries are usually black, hence the Hawaiian name *pōpolo*, which also refers to *Solanum americanum*, a notable source of traditional Hawaiian medicinal material. *Solanum nelsonii* is an endemic plant named after David Nelson, the British botanist on Captain James Cook's third voyage to the Pacific.

Distribution

Pōpolo is found in coastal sites from sea level up to about 500 feet, in sand or coral rubble. It has been collected in the past from sites on 6 of the main islands and several of the smaller ones. It is still common on many of the Northwestern Hawaiian Islands. On the main islands, *pōpolo* is now quite rare with the only large population at Moʻomomi, Molokaʻi. See the top photograph, where it is shown at that location, occuring with the common, indigenous, coastal plant *naupaka kahakai* (*Scaevola taccada*).

Limu **Seaweeds**

Various kinds of seaweeds (marine algae) are found in the ocean along the coastlines of Hawai'i. Although the word *limu* actually refers to a wide variety of plants that live under fresh and sea water, or in damp places, to many people in Hawai'i today *limu* simply means edible seaweed. Seaweeds are nonvascular, aquatic plants. Surrounded by water, they absorb necessary nutrients through their blades. About 450 species of seaweeds are found in the coastal waters of the Hawaiian Islands. Most are indigenous, along with some endemic and some alien species. Many have long been used for food, medicine, and other purposes in Hawai'i.

Limu 'aki'aki **(I)**
Ahnfeltia concinna

Limu 'aki'aki is a seaweed that grows upright 6 to 12 inches tall. Its densely bunched, tough, rubbery, cylindrical branches are 1 to 25 inches long. They vary in color from bright yellow on the highest growing individuals, to dark red on the lowest growing individuals. *Limu 'aki'aki* is found on *pāhoehoe* lava rock near the shore. Its name, *'aki'aki* refers to "the small bites necessary to chew it." It is sometimes added to chicken and fish baked in underground ovens (*imu*), or eaten along with *'opihi* (marine snail) and some cooked meats.

***Limu pālahalaha* (I)**
Sea Lettuce
Ulva fasciata

The sea lettuce, *limu pālahalaha*, resembles a lettuce leaf at the base with flat, tapering, ribbon-like, often twisted blades, ½ to 4 inches wide and 2 to 30 inches in length or longer. These are pale green in color when young, becoming darker green as they age. *Ulva lactuca*, which is closely related to *Ulva fasciata*, the species shown here, has broader blades. Another closely related species, *Ulva reticulata*, has thinner and more entangled blades with holes of various sizes, giving it a punched-out appearance. *Limu pālahalaha* is fairly common in the intertidal zones of Hawai'i. It is generally found on lava boulders and older corals, or on reef flats. It is frequently abundant in nutrient-rich environments. Washed and chpped up, this seaweed is added to other *limu* species and served with raw fish, or is cooked with other foods or soup. Braided as a *lei*, it was used to indicate that a visit had been made to a certain beach such as Polihale, Kaua'i.

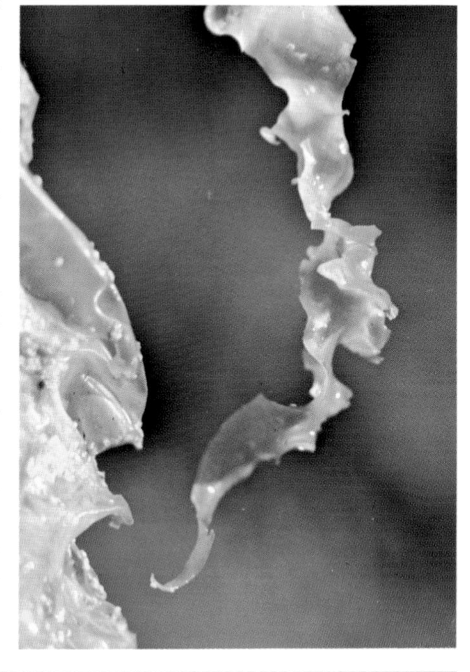

***Limu kala*, *'akala* (I)**
Sargassum echinocarpum

Description and Distribution

Limu kala is an indigenous marine algae. Technically, it is brown seaweed (division Phaeophyta) that grows about 10 to 20 inches high out of a relatively thick base. Its golden to dark brown leaf-like blades have a mid-rib and flattened stems. The blades grow to lengths of 1 to 4 (or more) inches and usually have "teeth" or serrations on their edges (margins). The blades are normally spiny, but smooth ones may be found. Small, inflated gas bladders with flattened stalks are often produced by this species. Two kinds of *limu kala* are traditionally recognized in Hawai`i. These are *kala lau li`i,* with small blades, and *kala lau nui,* with larger blades. This species of seaweed is found in various rocky and sandy marine areas found along the coasts of the Hawaiian Islands.

Uses and Other Species of *Limu Kala*

One of the marine species that feeds on *limu kala* is the trigger fish, known in Hawaiian as *kala*. Perhaps this provides us with a hint as to the origin of its name? However, the *kala* fish may also be associated with *pua kala*, the prickly poppy (see page 20). *Limu kala* has been, and still is, eaten in the Hawaiian Islands, although rarely because of its toughness. It is also used for fish bait, medicinal purposes, ornament, and in association with certain Hawaiian ceremonies involved with the removal of evil influences and obtaining forgiveness. Two additional species of seaweed in the genus *Sargassum* (*S. obtusifolium* and *S. polyphyllum*) are also found in marine environments of the Hawaiian Islands. Both species are also referred to in Hawaiian as *limu kala*.

Ornamentals

Over the years since the Polynesian islands of Hawai'i were contacted by the outside world in the 18th century, a large number of plant species have been introduced. Many of these alien species were brought here and cultivated for their ornamental attraction. The three decorative plants shown here, *Bouganvilllea* and *Hibiscus* (above), and *Plumeria* (below) are some of the most common and popular species planted for their showy flowers.

A Short List of References for Further Study

Abbott, Isabella A. 1992. *Lā'au Hawai'i: Traditional Hawaiian Uses of Plants.* Bishop Museum Press, Honolulu, Hawai'i. 163 pp.
Carlquist, Sherwin. 1980. *Hawaii A Natural History.* Pacific Tropical Botanical Garden, Lawai, Kaua'i. 2nd Edition. 468 pp.
Krauss, Beatrice H. 1993. *Plants in Hawaiian Culture.* University of Hawaii Press. Honolulu, Hawaii. 345 pp.
Lamoureux, Charles. 1996. *Trailside Plants of Hawaii's National Parks.* Hawai'i Natural History Association, Hawai'i. 2nd Edition. 79 pp.
Merlin, Mark. 1999. *Hawaiian Forest Plants.* Pacific Guide Books. Honolulu, Hawai'i. 68 pp., 5th edition
Neal, Marie C. 1965. *In Gardens of Hawaii.* Bishop Museum Press, Honolulu, Hawaii. 924 pp.
Sohmer, S.H. and Robert Gustafson. 1987. *Plants and Flowers of Hawai'i.* University of Hawai'i Press, Honolulu, Hawai'i. 160 pp.
Wagner, Warren L., Herbst, Derral R. and S.H. Sohmer. 1990. *Manual of the Flowering Plants of Hawai'i.* Bishop Museum Spec. Pub. 83. UH Press and Bishop Museum Press, Honolulu, Hawaii. 2 Vols., 1,853 pp.
Whistler, W. Arthur. 1992. *Flowers of the Pacific Island Seashore.* Isle Botanica, Honolulu, Hawai'i. 154 pp.

Published by Pacific Guide Books
1259C Center St., Honolulu, Hawai'i 96816
Printed by China Color Printing Co., Inc.
Taipei, Taiwan, Rep. of China
Revised 4th Edition 1999